Cover photograph
Mark Elder, the conductor
JANE CORSELLIS
The Bridgeman Art Library

Published in England by
FOUR SEASONS PUBLISHING LIMITED
16 ORCHARD RISE, KINGSTON UPON THAMES,
SURREY, KT2 7EY

Designed by Judith Pedersen
Printed in Singapore

Copyright © 2002 Four Seasons Publishing Ltd

ISBN: 1 85645 158 5

MUSICAL MEMO BOOK

FOUR SEASONS
PUBLISHING

*Music, be it Beethoven, Bartok or the Beatles,
brings us together in a sharing of sound.*
YEHUDI MENUHIN

Title:

Composer:

Soloist/Artist:

Recording:

When and where heard:

Notes:

Title:

Composer:

Soloist/Artist:

Recording:

When and where heard:

Notes:

Title:

Composer:

Soloist/Artist:

Recording:

When and where heard:

Notes:

> *The music in my heart I bore,*
> *Long after it was heard no more.*
> *WILLIAM WORDSWORTH*

Title:

Composer:

Soloist/Artist:

Recording:

When and where heard:

Notes:

Title:

Composer:

Soloist/Artist:

Recording:

When and where heard:

Notes:

Title:

Composer:

Soloist/Artist:

Recording:

When and where heard:

Notes:

> *Music and women I cannot but give way to,
> whatever my business is.*
> SAMUEL PEPYS

Title:

Composer:

Soloist/Artist:

Recording:

When and where heard:

Notes:

Title:

Composer:

Soloist/Artist:

Recording:

When and where heard:

Notes:

Title:

Composer:

Soloist/Artist:

Recording:

When and where heard:

Notes:

*Life seems to go on without effort
when I am filled with music.*
GEORGE ELIOT

Title:

Composer:

Soloist/Artist:

Recording:

When and where heard:

Notes:

Title:

Composer:

Soloist/Artist:

Recording:

When and where heard:

Notes:

Title:

Composer:

Soloist/Artist:

Recording:

When and where heard:

Notes:

> *M*usic alone with sudden charms can bind
> *T*he wand'ring sense, and calm the troubled mind.
> *WILLIAM CONGREVE*

Title:

Composer:

Soloist/Artist:

Recording:

When and where heard:

Notes:

Title:

Composer:

Soloist/Artist:

Recording:

When and where heard:

Notes:

Title:

Composer:

Soloist/Artist:

Recording:

When and where heard:

Notes:

– 10 –

There is really only one quality of great music and that is emotion.
FREDERICK DELIUS

Title:

Composer:

Soloist/Artist:

Recording:

When and where heard:

Notes:

Title:

Composer:

Soloist/Artist:

Recording:

When and where heard:

Notes:

Title:

Composer:

Soloist/Artist:

Recording:

When and where heard:

Notes:

Rock'n'Roll is just entertainment.
BILL HALEY

Title:

Composer:

Soloist/Artist:

Recording:

When and where heard:

Notes:

Title:

Composer:

Soloist/Artist:

Recording:

When and where heard:

Notes:

Title:

Composer:

Soloist/Artist:

Recording:

When and where heard:

Notes:

> *Music, when soft voices die,*
> *Vibrates in the memory.*
> PERCY BYSSHE SHELLEY

Title:

Composer:

Soloist/Artist:

Recording:

When and where heard:

Notes:

Title:

Composer:

Soloist/Artist:

Recording:

When and where heard:

Notes:

Title:

Composer:

Soloist/Artist:

Recording:

When and where heard:

Notes:

> *The world changes when there's music in it.*
> *It's transformed.*
> MICHAEL TILSON THOMAS

Title:

Composer:

Soloist/Artist:

Recording:

When and where heard:

Notes:

Title:

Composer:

Soloist/Artist:

Recording:

When and where heard:

Notes:

Title:

Composer:

Soloist/Artist:

Recording:

When and where heard:

Notes:

> *Music oft hath such a charm*
> *To make bad good, and good provoke to harm.*
> *WILLIAM SHAKESPEARE*

Title:

Composer:

Soloist/Artist:

Recording:

When and where heard:

Notes:

Title:

Composer:

Soloist/Artist:

Recording:

When and where heard:

Notes:

Title:

Composer:

Soloist/Artist:

Recording:

When and where heard:

Notes:

– 15 –

> *All* art constantly aspires towards
> the condition of music.
> *WALTER PATER*

Title:

Composer:

Soloist/Artist:

Recording:

When and where heard:

Notes:

Title:

Composer:

Soloist/Artist:

Recording:

When and where heard:

Notes:

Title:

Composer:

Soloist/Artist:

Recording:

When and where heard:

Notes:

We are the music makers,
We are the dreamers of dreams.
ARTHUR O'SHAUGHNESSY

Title:

Composer:

Soloist/Artist:

Recording:

When and where heard:

Notes:

Title:

Composer:

Soloist/Artist:

Recording:

When and where heard:

Notes:

Title:

Composer:

Soloist/Artist:

Recording:

When and where heard:

Notes:

> *The trumpet's loud clangour*
> *Excites us to arms.*
> JOHN DRYDEN

Title:

Composer:

Soloist/Artist:

Recording:

When and where heard:

Notes:

Title:

Composer:

Soloist/Artist:

Recording:

When and where heard:

Notes:

Title:

Composer:

Soloist/Artist:

Recording:

When and where heard:

Notes:

*There is delight in singing, tho' none hear
Beside the singer.*
WALTER SAVAGE LANDOR

Title:

Composer:

Soloist/Artist:

Recording:

When and where heard:

Notes:

Title:

Composer:

Soloist/Artist:

Recording:

When and where heard:

Notes:

Title:

Composer:

Soloist/Artist:

Recording:

When and where heard:

Notes:

> *A musicologist is a man who can read music
> but can't hear it.*
> SIR THOMAS BEECHAM

Title:

Composer:

Soloist/Artist:

Recording:

When and where heard:

Notes:

Title:

Composer:

Soloist/Artist:

Recording:

When and where heard:

Notes:

Title:

Composer:

Soloist/Artist:

Recording:

When and where heard:

Notes:

> *You ain't heard nothin' yet, folks.*
> *AL JOLSON*

Title:

Composer:

Soloist/Artist:

Recording:

When and where heard:

Notes:

Title:

Composer:

Soloist/Artist:

Recording:

When and where heard:

Notes:

Title:

Composer:

Soloist/Artist:

Recording:

When and where heard:

Notes:

*Music finds its way where
the rays of the sun cannot penetrate.*
SOREN KIERKEGAARD

Title:

Composer:

Soloist/Artist:

Recording:

When and where heard:

Notes:

Title:

Composer:

Soloist/Artist:

Recording:

When and where heard:

Notes:

Title:

Composer:

Soloist/Artist:

Recording:

When and where heard:

Notes:

> *T*he audience are the only smart people
> in show business.
> *RICHARD RODGERS*

Title:

Composer:

Soloist/Artist:

Recording:

When and where heard:

Notes:

Title:

Composer:

Soloist/Artist:

Recording:

When and where heard:

Notes:

Title:

Composer:

Soloist/Artist:

Recording:

When and where heard:

Notes:

> *Rock music has become an essential part
> of contemporary culture.*
> PHIL COLLINS

Title:

Composer:

Soloist/Artist:

Recording:

When and where heard:

Notes:

Title:

Composer:

Soloist/Artist:

Recording:

When and where heard:

Notes:

Title:

Composer:

Soloist/Artist:

Recording:

When and where heard:

Notes:

Country music deals with real human emotions and I'd say that's something we're all craving right now.
K.D. LANG

Title:

Composer:

Soloist/Artist:

Recording:

When and where heard:

Notes:

Title:

Composer:

Soloist/Artist:

Recording:

When and where heard:

Notes:

Title:

Composer:

Soloist/Artist:

Recording:

When and where heard:

Notes:

> *Do you know what my favourite musical sound in the world is? It's the sound of an orchestra tuning up.*
> ANDRE PREVIN

Title:

Composer:

Soloist/Artist:

Recording:

When and where heard:

Notes:

Title:

Composer:

Soloist/Artist:

Recording:

When and where heard:

Notes:

Title:

Composer:

Soloist/Artist:

Recording:

When and where heard:

Notes:

> *To learn to bring what character you have
> into sound takes a whole life.*
> *BUD FREEMAN*

Title:

Composer:

Soloist/Artist:

Recording:

When and where heard:

Notes:

Title:

Composer:

Soloist/Artist:

Recording:

When and where heard:

Notes:

Title:

Composer:

Soloist/Artist:

Recording:

When and where heard:

Notes:

> *T*hough music be a universal language, it is
> spoken with all sorts of accents.
> *BERNARD SHAW*

Title:

Composer:

Soloist/Artist:

Recording:

When and where heard:

Notes:

Title:

Composer:

Soloist/Artist:

Recording:

When and where heard:

Notes:

Title:

Composer:

Soloist/Artist:

Recording:

When and where heard:

Notes:

> *In an orchestra, with sufficient numbers,
> what one fails to perform is done by others.*
> HECTOR BERLIOZ

Title:

Composer:

Soloist/Artist:

Recording:

When and where heard:

Notes:

Title:

Composer:

Soloist/Artist:

Recording:

When and where heard:

Notes:

Title:

Composer:

Soloist/Artist:

Recording:

When and where heard:

Notes:

The principal merit of a good orchestral player consists of being subordinate.
LOUIS SPOHR

Title:

Composer:

Soloist/Artist:

Recording:

When and where heard:

Notes:

Title:

Composer:

Soloist/Artist:

Recording:

When and where heard:

Notes:

Title:

Composer:

Soloist/Artist:

Recording:

When and where heard:

Notes:

Conductors before everything else must be experts in aeroplane schedules and international tax laws.
IGOR STRAVINSKY

Title:

Composer:

Soloist/Artist:

Recording:

When and where heard:

Notes:

Title:

Composer:

Soloist/Artist:

Recording:

When and where heard:

Notes:

Title:

Composer:

Soloist/Artist:

Recording:

When and where heard:

Notes:

If the ruler's love of music were very great, then the kingdom would come near to being well governed.
MENCIUS

Title:

Composer:

Soloist/Artist:

Recording:

When and where heard:

Notes:

Title:

Composer:

Soloist/Artist:

Recording:

When and where heard:

Notes:

Title:

Composer:

Soloist/Artist:

Recording:

When and where heard:

Notes:

> *Ragtime became immortalized through Scott Joplin's dedication and talent.*
> *ITZHAK PERLMAN*

Title:

Composer:

Soloist/Artist:

Recording:

When and where heard:

Notes:

Title:

Composer:

Soloist/Artist:

Recording:

When and where heard:

Notes:

Title:

Composer:

Soloist/Artist:

Recording:

When and where heard:

Notes:

> *Will the people in the cheaper seats clap your hands?*
> *All the rest of you, just rattle your jewellery.*
> *JOHN LENNON*

Title:

Composer:

Soloist/Artist:

Recording:

When and where heard:

Notes:

Title:

Composer:

Soloist/Artist:

Recording:

When and where heard:

Notes:

Title:

Composer:

Soloist/Artist:

Recording:

When and where heard:

Notes:

> *Rock'n'Roll motivates. It's the big, gigantic, motivator, at least it was for me.*
> BRUCE SPRINGSTEEN

Title:

Composer:

Soloist/Artist:

Recording:

When and where heard:

Notes:

Title:

Composer:

Soloist/Artist:

Recording:

When and where heard:

Notes:

Title:

Composer:

Soloist/Artist:

Recording:

When and where heard:

Notes:

*E*motions *are universal, and music is the*
universal language.
HANS ZIMMER

Title:

Composer:

Soloist/Artist:

Recording:

When and where heard:

Notes:

Title:

Composer:

Soloist/Artist:

Recording:

When and where heard:

Notes:

Title:

Composer:

Soloist/Artist:

Recording:

When and where heard:

Notes:

> *F*ilm music is like a small lamp that you
> place below the screen to warm it.
> *AARON COPLAND*

Title:

Composer:

Soloist/Artist:

Recording:

When and where heard:

Notes:

Title:

Composer:

Soloist/Artist:

Recording:

When and where heard:

Notes:

Title:

Composer:

Soloist/Artist:

Recording:

When and where heard:

Notes:

*There is sweet music here that softer falls
Than petals from blown roses on the grass…*
ALFRED LORD TENNYSON

Title:

Composer:

Soloist/Artist:

Recording:

When and where heard:

Notes:

Title:

Composer:

Soloist/Artist:

Recording:

When and where heard:

Notes:

Title:

Composer:

Soloist/Artist:

Recording:

When and where heard:

Notes:

> *I guess all songs is folk songs.*
> *I never heard no horse sing 'em.*
> LOUIS ARMSTRONG

Title:

Composer:

Soloist/Artist:

Recording:

When and where heard:

Notes:

Title:

Composer:

Soloist/Artist:

Recording:

When and where heard:

Notes:

Title:

Composer:

Soloist/Artist:

Recording:

When and where heard:

Notes:

The blues is both music and the feeling that inspires it.
NEIL SLAVEN

Title:

Composer:

Soloist/Artist:

Recording:

When and where heard:

Notes:

Title:

Composer:

Soloist/Artist:

Recording:

When and where heard:

Notes:

Title:

Composer:

Soloist/Artist:

Recording:

When and where heard:

Notes:

*Jazz is the symbol of the triumph
of the human spirit.*
ARCHIE SHEPP

Title:

Composer:

Soloist/Artist:

Recording:

When and where heard:

Notes:

Title:

Composer:

Soloist/Artist:

Recording:

When and where heard:

Notes:

Title:

Composer:

Soloist/Artist:

Recording:

When and where heard:

Notes:

*The art of music above all the arts
is the expression of the soul of a nation.*
RALPH VAUGHAN WILLIAMS

Title:

Composer:

Soloist/Artist:

Recording:

When and where heard:

Notes:

Title:

Composer:

Soloist/Artist:

Recording:

When and where heard:

Notes:

Title:

Composer:

Soloist/Artist:

Recording:

When and where heard:

Notes:

> *I doff my cap and kneel at his grave.*
> LUDWIG VAN BEETHOVEN'S TRIBUTE TO HANDEL

Title:

Composer:

Soloist/Artist:

Recording:

When and where heard:

Notes:

Title:

Composer:

Soloist/Artist:

Recording:

When and where heard:

Notes:

Title:

Composer:

Soloist/Artist:

Recording:

When and where heard:

Notes:

> *I* read everything, played everything
> and heard everything I possibly could.
> EDWARD WILLIAM ELGAR

Title:

Composer:

Soloist/Artist:

Recording:

When and where heard:

Notes:

Title:

Composer:

Soloist/Artist:

Recording:

When and where heard:

Notes:

Title:

Composer:

Soloist/Artist:

Recording:

When and where heard:

Notes:

> *Whoever listens to my music intelligently,*
> *will see my life transparently revealed.*
> GUSTAV MAHLER

Title:

Composer:

Soloist/Artist:

Recording:

When and where heard:

Notes:

Title:

Composer:

Soloist/Artist:

Recording:

When and where heard:

Notes:

Title:

Composer:

Soloist/Artist:

Recording:

When and where heard:

Notes:

– 45 –

> *Madam, you have between your legs an
> instrument that can give pleasure to thousands.*
> *SIR THOMAS BEECHAM*

Title:

Composer:

Soloist/Artist:

Recording:

When and where heard:

Notes:

Title:

Composer:

Soloist/Artist:

Recording:

When and where heard:

Notes:

Title:

Composer:

Soloist/Artist:

Recording:

When and where heard:

Notes:

Title:

Composer:

Soloist/Artist:

Recording:

When and where heard:

Notes:

Title:

Composer:

Soloist/Artist:

Recording:

When and where heard:

Notes:

Title:

Composer:

Soloist/Artist:

Recording:

When and where heard:

Notes:

– 47 –

> *I wish to become a Mozart in composition and a Liszt in technique.*
> *BEDRICH SMETANA*

Title:

Composer:

Soloist/Artist:

Recording:

When and where heard:

Notes:

Title:

Composer:

Soloist/Artist:

Recording:

When and where heard:

Notes:

Title:

Composer:

Soloist/Artist:

Recording:

When and where heard:

Notes:

I like Wagner's music. It's so loud that one can talk the whole time without people hearing what one says.
OSCAR WILDE

Title:

Composer:

Soloist/Artist:

Recording:

When and where heard:

Notes:

Title:

Composer:

Soloist/Artist:

Recording:

When and where heard:

Notes:

Title:

Composer:

Soloist/Artist:

Recording:

When and where heard:

Notes:

> *The first requirement of a composer is to be dead.*
> ARTHUR HONEGGER

Title:

Composer:

Soloist/Artist:

Recording:

When and where heard:

Notes:

Title:

Composer:

Soloist/Artist:

Recording:

When and where heard:

Notes:

Title:

Composer:

Soloist/Artist:

Recording:

When and where heard:

Notes:

> ## *Music is an outburst of the soul.*
> *FREDERICK DELIUS*

Title:

Composer:

Soloist/Artist:

Recording:

When and where heard:

Notes:

Title:

Composer:

Soloist/Artist:

Recording:

When and where heard:

Notes:

Title:

Composer:

Soloist/Artist:

Recording:

When and where heard:

Notes:

– 51 –

After silence, that which comes nearest to expressing the inexpressible is music.
ALDOUS HUXLEY

Title:

Composer:

Soloist/Artist:

Recording:

When and where heard:

Notes:

Title:

Composer:

Soloist/Artist:

Recording:

When and where heard:

Notes:

Title:

Composer:

Soloist/Artist:

Recording:

When and where heard:

Notes:

Title:

Composer:

Soloist/Artist:

Recording:

When and where heard:

Notes:

Title:

Composer:

Soloist/Artist:

Recording:

When and where heard:

Notes:

Title:

Composer:

Soloist/Artist:

Recording:

When and where heard:

Notes:

Gloomy cares will be lightened by song.
HORACE

Title:

Composer:

Soloist/Artist:

Recording:

When and where heard:

Notes:

Title:

Composer:

Soloist/Artist:

Recording:

When and where heard:

Notes:

Title:

Composer:

Soloist/Artist:

Recording:

When and where heard:

Notes:

He who sings scares away his woes.
CERVANTES

Title:

Composer:

Soloist/Artist:

Recording:

When and where heard:

Notes:

Title:

Composer:

Soloist/Artist:

Recording:

When and where heard:

Notes:

Title:

Composer:

Soloist/Artist:

Recording:

When and where heard:

Notes:

> *If I were to begin life again,*
> *I would devote it to music.*
> SYDNEY SMITH

Title:

Composer:

Soloist/Artist:

Recording:

When and where heard:

Notes:

Title:

Composer:

Soloist/Artist:

Recording:

When and where heard:

Notes:

Title:

Composer:

Soloist/Artist:

Recording:

When and where heard:

Notes:

*I*s there a heart that music cannot melt?
JAMES BEATTIE

Title:

Composer:

Soloist/Artist:

Recording:

When and where heard:

Notes:

Title:

Composer:

Soloist/Artist:

Recording:

When and where heard:

Notes:

Title:

Composer:

Soloist/Artist:

Recording:

When and where heard:

Notes:

> *I think I should have no other mortal wants,*
> *if I could always have plenty of music.*
> GEORGE ELIOT

Title:

Composer:

Soloist/Artist:

Recording:

When and where heard:

Notes:

Title:

Composer:

Soloist/Artist:

Recording:

When and where heard:

Notes:

Title:

Composer:

Soloist/Artist:

Recording:

When and where heard:

Notes:

It is the best of all trades to make songs,
and the second best to sing them.
HILAIRE BELLOC

Title:

Composer:

Soloist/Artist:

Recording:

When and where heard:

Notes:

Title:

Composer:

Soloist/Artist:

Recording:

When and where heard:

Notes:

Title:

Composer:

Soloist/Artist:

Recording:

When and where heard:

Notes:

Music is the only sensual pleasure without vice.
SAMUEL JOHNSON

Title:

Composer:

Soloist/Artist:

Recording:

When and where heard:

Notes:

Title:

Composer:

Soloist/Artist:

Recording:

When and where heard:

Notes:

Title:

Composer:

Soloist/Artist:

Recording:

When and where heard:

Notes:

> *Jazz music is to be played sweet,*
> *soft, plenty rhythm.*
> *JELLY ROLL MORTON*

Title:

Composer:

Soloist/Artist:

Recording:

When and where heard:

Notes:

Title:

Composer:

Soloist/Artist:

Recording:

When and where heard:

Notes:

Title:

Composer:

Soloist/Artist:

Recording:

When and where heard:

Notes:

> *Music and rhythm find their way
> into the secret places of the soul.*
> PLATO

Title:

Composer:

Soloist/Artist:

Recording:

When and where heard:

Notes:

Title:

Composer:

Soloist/Artist:

Recording:

When and where heard:

Notes:

Title:

Composer:

Soloist/Artist:

Recording:

When and where heard:

Notes:

> *The song that we hear with our ears
> is only the song that is sung in our hearts.*
> OUIDA

Title:

Composer:

Soloist/Artist:

Recording:

When and where heard:

Notes:

Title:

Composer:

Soloist/Artist:

Recording:

When and where heard:

Notes:

Title:

Composer:

Soloist/Artist:

Recording:

When and where heard:

Notes:

> *Musicians don't retire, they stop
> when there's no more music in them.*
> LOUIS ARMSTRONG

Title:

Composer:

Soloist/Artist:

Recording:

When and where heard:

Notes:

Title:

Composer:

Soloist/Artist:

Recording:

When and where heard:

Notes:

Title:

Composer:

Soloist/Artist:

Recording:

When and where heard:

Notes:

*The hills are alive with the sound of music,
With the songs they have sung for a thousand years.*
OSCAR HAMMERSTEIN

Title:

Composer:

Soloist/Artist:

Recording:

When and where heard:

Notes:

Title:

Composer:

Soloist/Artist:

Recording:

When and where heard:

Notes:

Title:

Composer:

Soloist/Artist:

Recording:

When and where heard:

Notes:

*Music expresses that which cannot be put into words
and that which cannot remain silent.*
VICTOR HUGO

Title:

Composer:

Soloist/Artist:

Recording:

When and where heard:

Notes:

Title:

Composer:

Soloist/Artist:

Recording:

When and where heard:

Notes:

Title:

Composer:

Soloist/Artist:

Recording:

When and where heard:

Notes:

> *Music first and last should sound well,
> should allure and enchant the ear.*
> SIR THOMAS BEECHAM

Title:

Composer:

Soloist/Artist:

Recording:

When and where heard:

Notes:

Title:

Composer:

Soloist/Artist:

Recording:

When and where heard:

Notes:

Title:

Composer:

Soloist/Artist:

Recording:

When and where heard:

Notes:

> *Without music life would be a mistake.*
> FRIEDRICH NIETZSCHE

Title:

Composer:

Soloist/Artist:

Recording:

When and where heard:

Notes:

Title:

Composer:

Soloist/Artist:

Recording:

When and where heard:

Notes:

Title:

Composer:

Soloist/Artist:

Recording:

When and where heard:

Notes:

Music is like the work of an artist painting in sounds, with the colour in harmony.

GEORGE MARTIN

Title:

Composer:

Soloist/Artist:

Recording:

When and where heard:

Notes:

Title:

Composer:

Soloist/Artist:

Recording:

When and where heard:

Notes:

Title:

Composer:

Soloist/Artist:

Recording:

When and where heard:

Notes:

– 69 –

> *Alas for those that never sing,*
> *But die with all their music in them!*
> OLIVER WENDELL HOLMES

Title:

Composer:

Soloist/Artist:

Recording:

When and where heard:

Notes:

Title:

Composer:

Soloist/Artist:

Recording:

When and where heard:

Notes:

Title:

Composer:

Soloist/Artist:

Recording:

When and where heard:

Notes:

> *Music is the only language in which you cannot say a mean or sarcastic thing.*
> *JOHN ERSKINE*

Title:

Composer:

Soloist/Artist:

Recording:

When and where heard:

Notes:

Title:

Composer:

Soloist/Artist:

Recording:

When and where heard:

Notes:

Title:

Composer:

Soloist/Artist:

Recording:

When and where heard:

Notes:

– 71 –

*M*usic is the universal language of mankind.
HENRY WADSWORTH LONGFELLOW

Title:

Composer:

Soloist/Artist:

Recording:

When and where heard:

Notes:

Title:

Composer:

Soloist/Artist:

Recording:

When and where heard:

Notes:

Title:

Composer:

Soloist/Artist:

Recording:

When and where heard:

Notes:

*Music washes away from the soul
the dust of everyday life.*
AUERBACH

Title:

Composer:

Soloist/Artist:

Recording:

When and where heard:

Notes:

Title:

Composer:

Soloist/Artist:

Recording:

When and where heard:

Notes:

Title:

Composer:

Soloist/Artist:

Recording:

When and where heard:

Notes:

> *The great musicians are the ones who can observe
> life and then crystallise this down into a little tune.*
> *MICHAEL TILSON THOMAS*

Title:

Composer:

Soloist/Artist:

Recording:

When and where heard:

Notes:

Title:

Composer:

Soloist/Artist:

Recording:

When and where heard:

Notes:

Title:

Composer:

Soloist/Artist:

Recording:

When and where heard:

Notes:

*E*lvis was bigger than religion in my life.
JOHN LENNON

Title:

Composer:

Soloist/Artist:

Recording:

When and where heard:

Notes:

Title:

Composer:

Soloist/Artist:

Recording:

When and where heard:

Notes:

Title:

Composer:

Soloist/Artist:

Recording:

When and where heard:

Notes:

> *Melody is the absolute language in which*
> *the musician speaks to every heart.*
> RICHARD WAGNER

Title:

Composer:

Soloist/Artist:

Recording:

When and where heard:

Notes:

Title:

Composer:

Soloist/Artist:

Recording:

When and where heard:

Notes:

Title:

Composer:

Soloist/Artist:

Recording:

When and where heard:

Notes:

> *There is music in the air,*
> *music all around us.*
> EDWARD WILLIAM ELGAR

Title:

Composer:

Soloist/Artist:

Recording:

When and where heard:

Notes:

Title:

Composer:

Soloist/Artist:

Recording:

When and where heard:

Notes:

Title:

Composer:

Soloist/Artist:

Recording:

When and where heard:

Notes:

*M*usic exalts each joy, allays each grief.
JOHN ARMSTRONG

Title:

Composer:

Soloist/Artist:

Recording:

When and where heard:

Notes:

Title:

Composer:

Soloist/Artist:

Recording:

When and where heard:

Notes:

Title:

Composer:

Soloist/Artist:

Recording:

When and where heard:

Notes:

There's sure no passion in the human soul
but finds its food in music.
GEORGE LILLO

Title:

Composer:

Soloist/Artist:

Recording:

When and where heard:

Notes:

Title:

Composer:

Soloist/Artist:

Recording:

When and where heard:

Notes:

Title:

Composer:

Soloist/Artist:

Recording:

When and where heard:

Notes:

> *We use music to change our emotions.*
> JOHN SLOBODA

Title:

Composer:

Soloist/Artist:

Recording:

When and where heard:

Notes:

Title:

Composer:

Soloist/Artist:

Recording:

When and where heard:

Notes:

Title:

Composer:

Soloist/Artist:

Recording:

When and where heard:

Notes:

Music and life are one indivisible breath expressing everything we know and feel.
YEHUDI MENUHIN

Title:

Composer:

Soloist/Artist:

Recording:

When and where heard:

Notes:

Title:

Composer:

Soloist/Artist:

Recording:

When and where heard:

Notes:

Title:

Composer:

Soloist/Artist:

Recording:

When and where heard:

Notes:

> *There is no truer truth obtainable*
> *by man than comes of music.*
> ROBERT BROWNING

Title:

Composer:

Soloist/Artist:

Recording:

When and where heard:

Notes:

Title:

Composer:

Soloist/Artist:

Recording:

When and where heard:

Notes:

Title:

Composer:

Soloist/Artist:

Recording:

When and where heard:

Notes:

*M*usic is the medicine of a troubled mind.
WALTER HADDON

Title:

Composer:

Soloist/Artist:

Recording:

When and where heard:

Notes:

Title:

Composer:

Soloist/Artist:

Recording:

When and where heard:

Notes:

Title:

Composer:

Soloist/Artist:

Recording:

When and where heard:

Notes:

> *In music one must think with the heart
> and feel with the brain.*
> GEORGE SZELL

Title:

Composer:

Soloist/Artist:

Recording:

When and where heard:

Notes:

Title:

Composer:

Soloist/Artist:

Recording:

When and where heard:

Notes:

Title:

Composer:

Soloist/Artist:

Recording:

When and where heard:

Notes:

The oboe has a pastoral character full of tenderness.
HECTOR BERLIOZ

Title:

Composer:

Soloist/Artist:

Recording:

When and where heard:

Notes:

Title:

Composer:

Soloist/Artist:

Recording:

When and where heard:

Notes:

Title:

Composer:

Soloist/Artist:

Recording:

When and where heard:

Notes:

Music, the greatest good that mortals know...
JOSEPH ADDISON

Title:

Composer:

Soloist/Artist:

Recording:

When and where heard:

Notes:

Title:

Composer:

Soloist/Artist:

Recording:

When and where heard:

Notes:

Title:

Composer:

Soloist/Artist:

Recording:

When and where heard:

Notes:

INDEX

Title	Composer	Page

INDEX

INDEX

Title	Composer	Page

INDEX

INDEX

Title	Composer	Page

INDEX

Title	Composer	Page

INDEX

Title	Composer	Page